First published in Great Britain 2014 by Egmont UK Limited,
1 Nicholas Road, London W11 4AN
Written by Catherine Shoolbred. Designed by Ruby Shoes Limited.

ISBN 978 1 4052 7132 5
57316/1
Printed in Italy

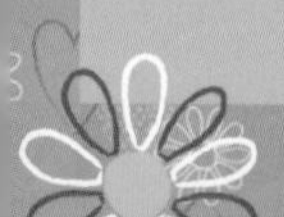

This

Holiday Annual

belongs to

____

____

Age ____________________

What's Inside ...

Meet Doc's Toy Team!
Doc is a little girl with a big secret – her magic stethoscope can bring toys to life. If a toy is feeling poorly, she can make them well again!
Just doin' my job!
Lambie likes dancing, but hates getting dirty. She cuddles poorly toys to help them feel better.
Need a cuddle?

Stuffy is always rushing around and falling over. He thinks he's brave, but really he's a scaredy dragon!

I meant to do that!

Hallie is very caring. She always has Doc's equipment ready so she can look after her toy patients.

Sweet sassy sunshine!

Stay Cool!

Chilly the snowman often forgets he's a toy and thinks he's going to melt!

How many hearts can you see?

Add the number in the box.

Answer: 5 hearts.

Spot the Difference

These pictures look the same but 6 things are different in picture 2. Can you spot them all?

1

2

Answers:

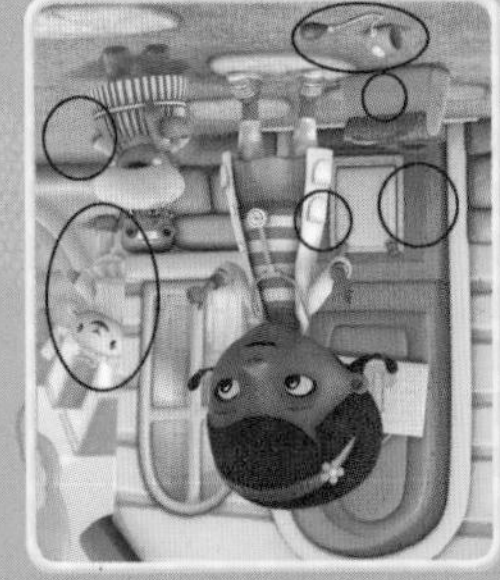

story

Knight Time

1

Doc and her toys are playing a make-believe game of Princesses and Knights.

2

Princess Lambie is trapped in a castle tower. If only there were a brave knight who could rescue her!

"Here I come," yells Stuffy. "A brave knight to the rescue-ooo-ouch!" Stuffy slips and lands with a thump.

3

4

Lambie isn't very impressed! "Doc, can't a real knight in shining armour rescue me for once?" she says.

5

"Donny used to have a toy knight, perhaps he can play our game?" wonders Doc.
"But what about me?" asks Stuffy.
"You're the scary dragon," says Doc.
"I'd be great at that! Rarrrr!" says Stuffy.

6

Doc asks Donny if she can borrow his knight. She finds him hidden under Donny's bed.

7

Doc uses her magic stethoscope to bring him to life. "Wow, a real knight in shining armour!" says Lambie.

8

"I am Sir Kirby, the bravest knight of them all! How may I serve you Princess Lambie?" he asks.

9

"I need rescuing from this scary dragon," says Lambie.
"Do not fear, I shall save yoooooouuu ... oops!"

10

"Sir Kirby? Are you okay?" asks Hallie.
"It seems my legs aren't working very well. Or my arms!" says Sir Kirby.
"Even my suit of armour doesn't shine any more. I'm a hopeless knight," he sighs.

Trace over the path to guide Sir Kirby back to his horse.

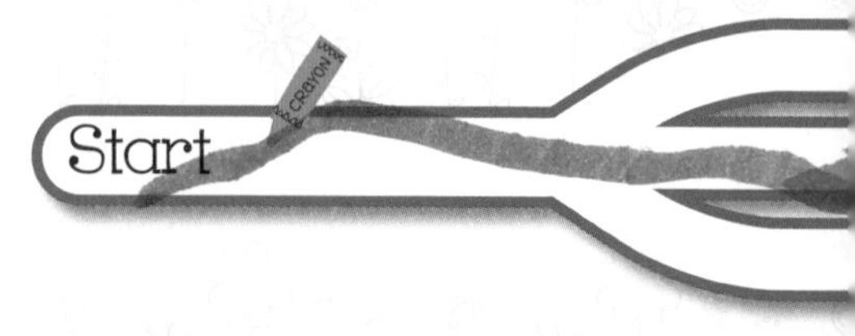

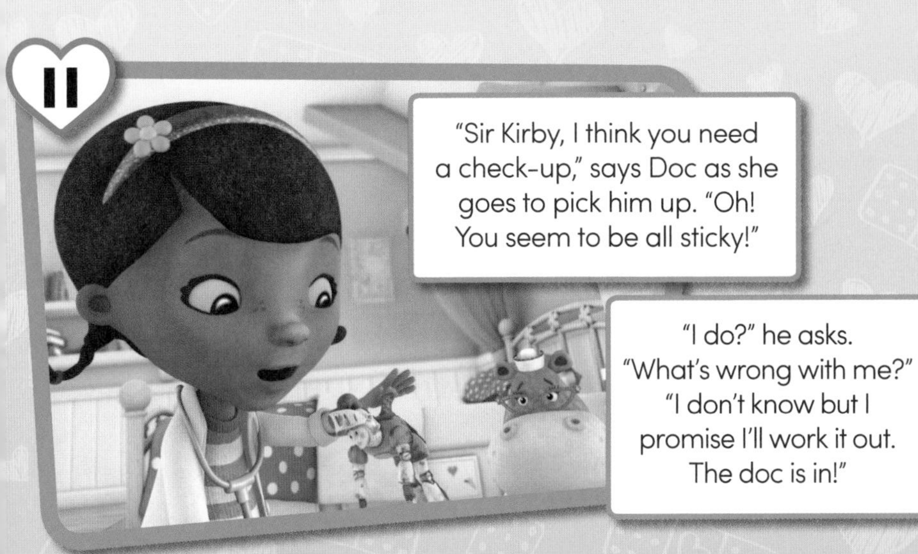

"What are those shiny things?" he asks nervously. "Don't worry, these are the tools I use to help my patients feel better."

"I'm checking your heart ... sounds good. Now stand against this wall so that I can measure you."

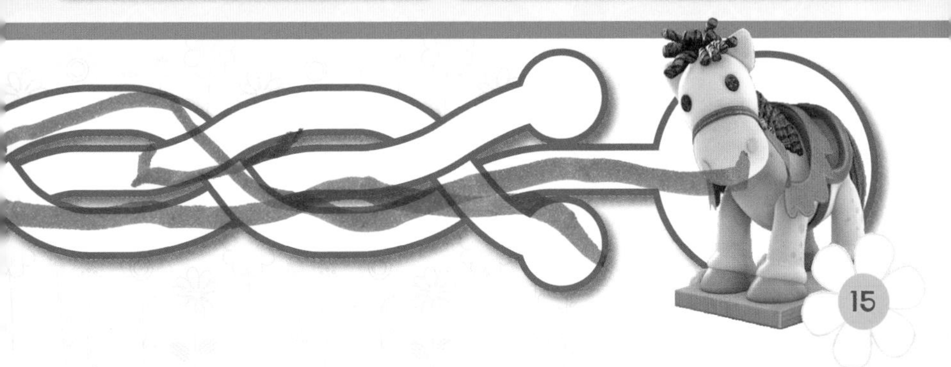

14

"Your height is good, you can step away now, Sir Kirby."
"I can't! I appear to be stuck!" he says.

15

Stuffy helps to unstick him from the wall. Doc examines his armour with her magnifying glass.

16

"Ew, it looks like you're covered in sticky jam and pizza cheese! Sir Kirby, when was the last time you had a bath?"

"A bath? I've never had a bath!"
"Sir Kirby, I have a diagnosis. You have Filthy-Icky-Sticky Disease!"

Let's sing together ...

If your face is dirty it's time for a scrub,
Run a bubble bath and rub-a-dub-dub!

17

"That should go in the Big Book of Boo Boos!" cries Hallie.
"But is there a cure?" asks Sir Kirby.
"You're covered in sticky food, that's why you're sticking to everything. It's time for a bath!" says Doc.

18

Doc's mum runs a bubble bath and Doc washes all the ickiness off Sir Kirby. Soon he's as good as new!

19

"I feel so much better," he cries. "Now I can rescue Princess Lambie!"
"Ah, my knight in shiny armour," says Lambie, and everybody laughs!

Doc's Bag Dot-to-Dot

Join the dots to complete Doc's bag! Then count up the plasters and write the number in the box.

Colour Stuffy

Finish colouring Stuffy as neatly as you can so Lambie can give him a cuddle!

What's in Doc's Bag?

Doc carries lots of tools that can help sick toys feel better. Follow the lines to find out what each ones does.

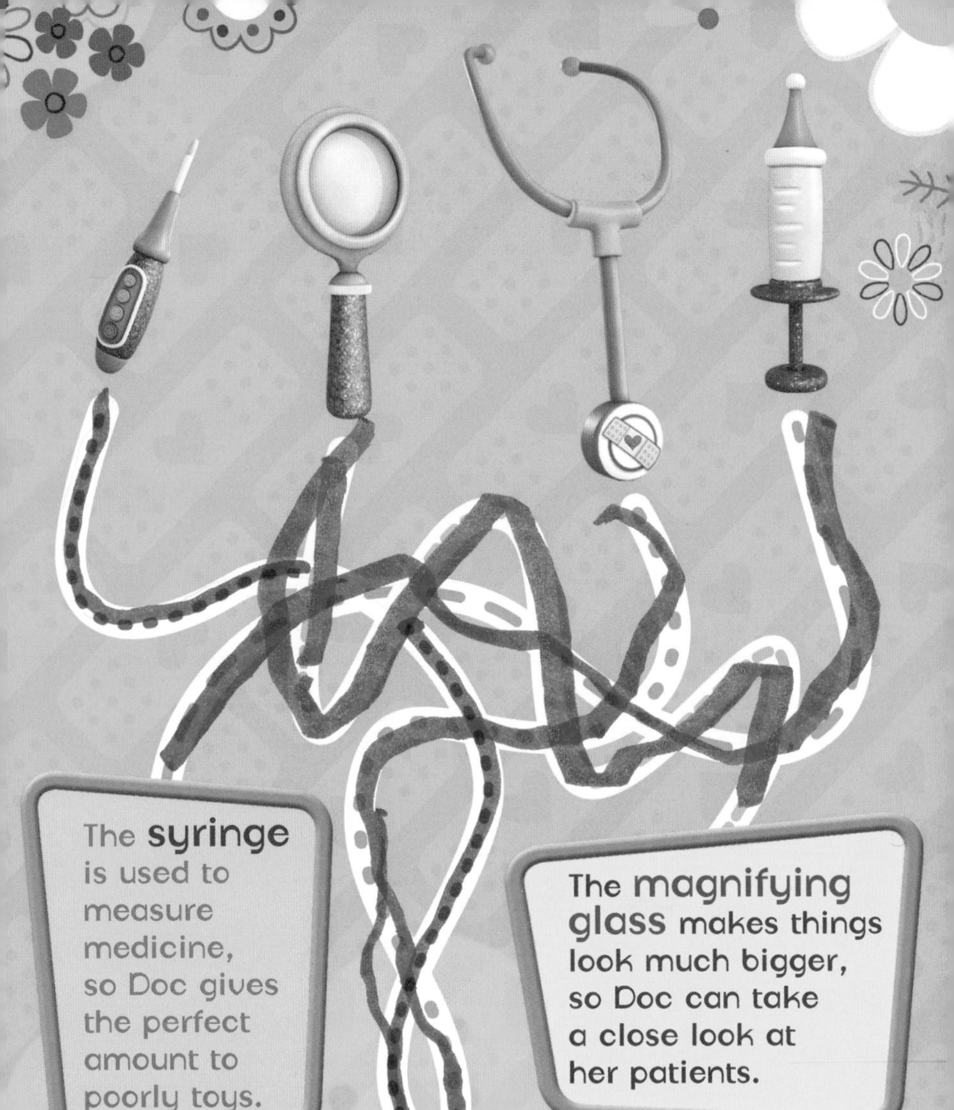

The **syringe** is used to measure medicine, so Doc gives the perfect amount to poorly toys.

The **magnifying glass** makes things look much bigger, so Doc can take a close look at her patients.

The **stethoscope** hears heartbeats. Doc's special one brings toys to life!

The **thermometer** measures your temperature, to check you're not too hot or too cold.

Doc's Diagnosis

Doc gives poorly toys a check-up to see what's wrong. Then she writes her diagnosis in the Big Book of Boo-Boos. Can you match the patients to their Boo-Boos?

a. No-Vroom-Vroom-a-tosis

b. Bronto Boo-Boos

c. Earstuffinosis

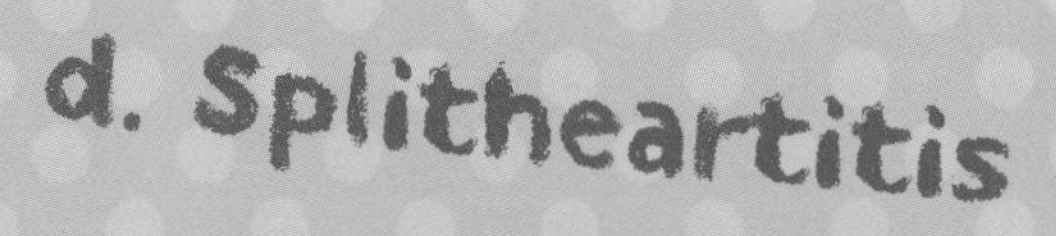

Answers: 1 = d, 2 = a, 3 = c, 4 = b.

Story

A Bad Case o

1

Donny and Will are playing in the garden with their toy, Boppy. Push him and he bops straight back up again!

2

Even Doc can't manage to bop him and make him stay down. He's just so bouncy!

3

Doc giggles as she walks to her surgery. Boppy is so funny! She says hi to all her toy friends. "Hi, Doc!" they shout.

Suddenly there's a knock at the door. "Toys, go stuffed!" says Doc as she opens the door. It's Donny and Will.

he Pricklethorns!

4

"Doc, can you help us?" asks Donny. "Boppy's got a hole and he's losing air! He doesn't bop back up any more."

"This sounds like an emergency!" says Doc. "If you let me examine him, I'll do everything I can to fix him."

Doc takes Boppy into the surgery and the toys rush to help her. She quickly magics Boppy to life.

5

6

"I don't feel good," Boppy groans. "Magnifying glass, please, Hallie!" says Doc as she examines her patient.

7

"I have to find the leak," says Doc as she examines Boppy. "There it is! Stuffy, I need you to press here."

8

"Okay!" says Stuffy as he puts his paws over the leak. "I did it!" "Great. Now I'll cover it with a plaster," says Doc.

9

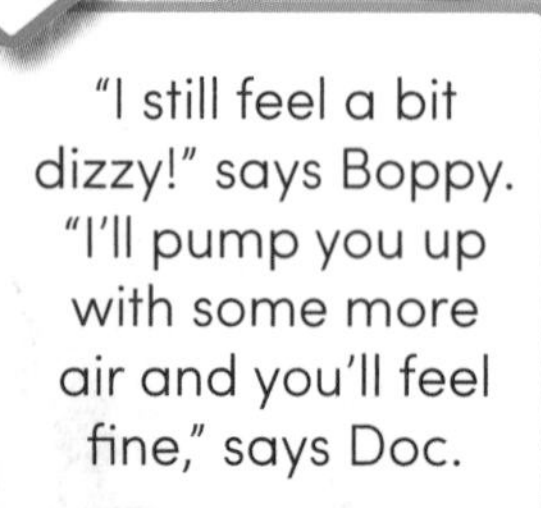

"I still feel a bit dizzy!" says Boppy. "I'll pump you up with some more air and you'll feel fine," says Doc.

"Thanks, Doc, I feel much better," says Boppy as he bounces around the surgery. "Let's play!"

Count how many times Boppy bounces through the garden.

Start

1

"I'll play!" says Stuffy and together they all run out into the garden.
"Bop! Bop! Bop!" goes Boppy.
Suddenly there's a loud HISSSSS.
"Oh no," says Doc. "I think Boppy is losing air again!"

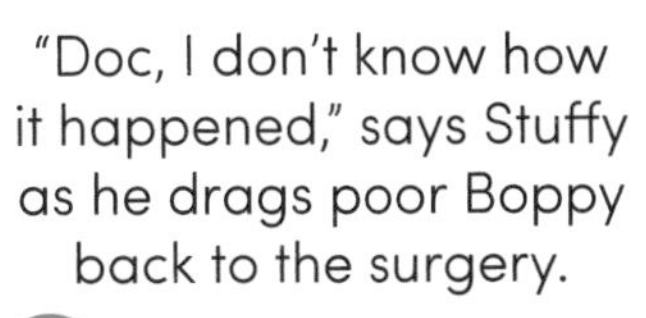

"Doc, I don't know how it happened," says Stuffy as he drags poor Boppy back to the surgery.

Doc quickly finds the new hole and sticks another plaster over it.

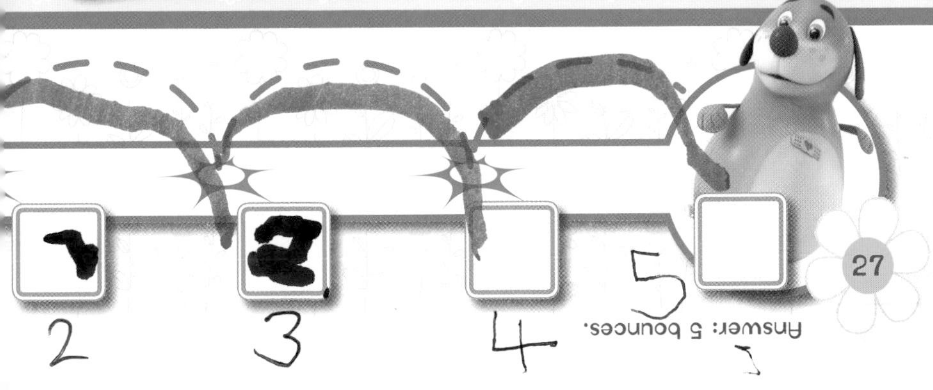

13

"You know, a doctor's job isn't just to help you after you're hurt," says Doc. "It's to help you not get hurt in the first place."

14

"Boppy, Stuffy, show me exactly what happened."
"We were playing over there," says Stuffy.

15

"You played by the rose bushes?" asks Doc. "Then I have a diagnosis!"
"What's wrong with me?" asks Boppy.

"You have a bad case of the pricklethorns!"
"And that goes right here in the Big Book of Boo-Boos!" says Hallie.

Let's say it together ...

Everyone gets hurt sometimes, so don't be afraid to ask for help!

16

"What does it mean?" asks Boppy. "It means you've pricked yourself on a thorn, or something sharp," says Doc.

"Oh! So how do I not get the pricklethorns again?" asks Boppy. "You should stay away from thorns and sharp things," says Doc.

17

"Toys, go stuffed! Here comes Donny and Will," says Doc. "Did you save Boppy?" they ask.

18

"He's as good as new. Play with him away from the rose bushes and he'll be fine," explains Doc. "Thanks Doc," they say. "You're the best!"

What's Wrong with Boppy?

After falling in a thorny rose, Boppy the blow-up dog had a hole in his side. Can you remember the right diagnosis for the Big Book of Boo-Boos?

a Shark-style Toothache

b A Bad Case of Pricklethorns

c A Good Case of Hiccups

Now draw Boppy and the rose for the Big Book of Boo-Boos.

Doc's Colourful Friends

Doc's toy friends come in all sorts of colours. Can you spot friends who are the following colours:

Who's Who?

Read about Doc and her friends, then write over their names so you know who's who.

1. I wear a white coat.
I have brown hair.
I make toys better.

Doc

2. I am blue.
I'm not very brave.
I have wings.

Stuffy

3. I wear a pink skirt.
I am woolly and white.
I love giving cuddles.

Lambie

4. I am a hippo.
I wear red glasses.
I help Doc with patients.

Hallie

Magnified Close-ups

Can you tell who's in these close-up pictures?

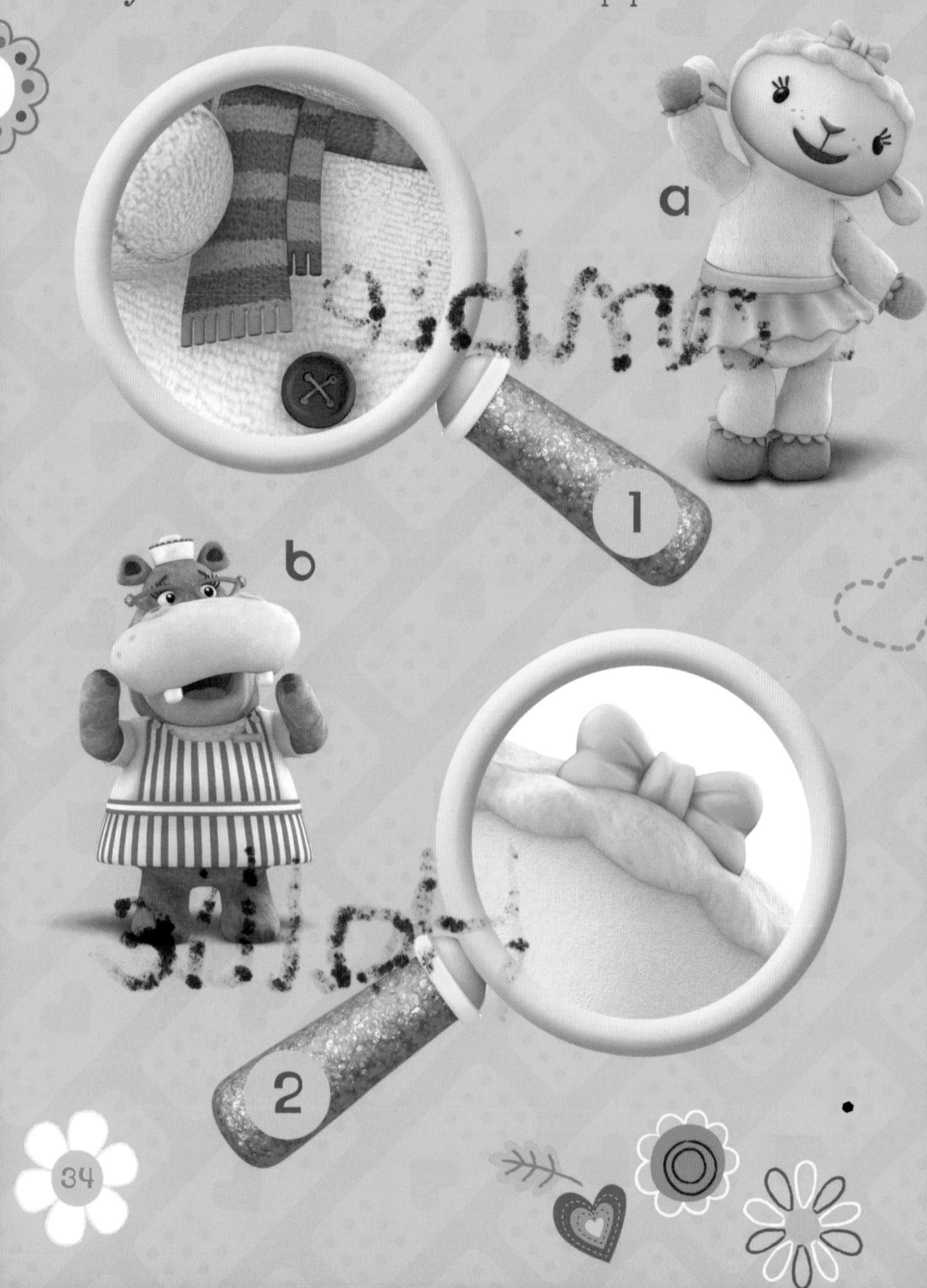

3

c

4

d

Answers: 1 = c, 2 = a, 3 = d, 4 = b.

Colour Time

Complete the picture of Doc and Lambie as neatly as you can.

What's Next?

Doc is making patterns today. Can you draw the next item in each row?

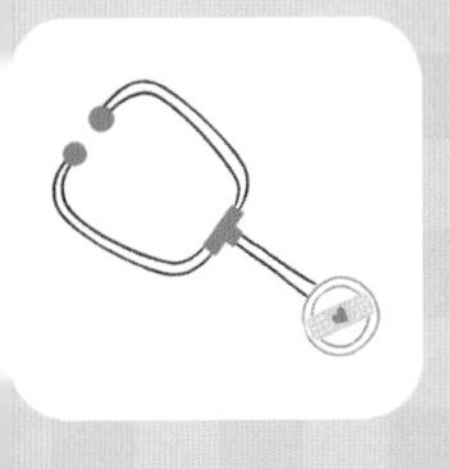

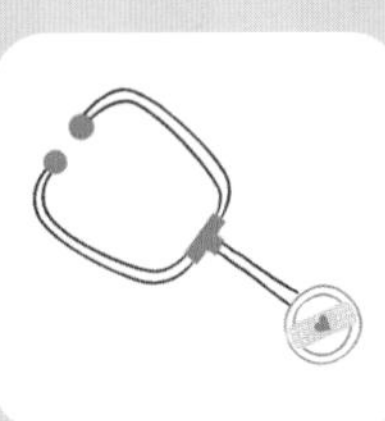

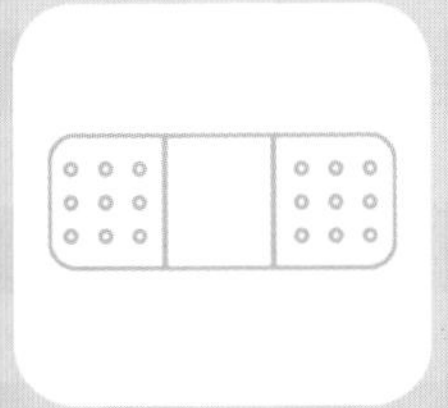

Doc's family are going to an amusement arcade. Doc and Donny can't wait to play their favourite games!

Donny wants to play the ball throwing game while Doc wants to play on the race car game.

She skips to the race car and touches her stethoscope to bring her toy friends to life.

Escapade!

"Lambie, you can help me steer!" giggles Doc as she presses the start button. "Ready to go, Stuffy?"
"Put your pedal to the metal, Doc!" he yells. "Whoo-hoo, let's go! Zoom zoom zoom, this is so fun!"

4

5

Suddenly Doc hears a noise. "Did somebody just call my name?" she asks.

6

Doc looks all around. It wasn't her dad calling her. Or Donny. Who could be shouting Doc's name?

7

"Doc, over here!" shouts the voice. "There it is again," says Stuffy. Doc, Stuffy and Lambie look all around.

8

"Look! It's coming from the toy grabber tank," says Doc. "It's the toys in the tank calling to me. Let's go!"

9

"Doc McStuffins? Is it really you?" asks a big pink bear. "It is! You can call me Doc," she smiles. "We've heard that you can fix toys and my friend Gaby the Giraffe really needs your help."

Which path should Doc take to reach Gaby?

Trace over it.

10
"Hi, Gaby," says Doc. "What's wrong?"
"A little girl tried to win me by picking me up with the big grabber," Gaby says.
"But the grabber dropped me and tore my leg. Now nobody wants to win me because I'm broken. I'm so upset!"
11
"It's okay, Gaby, I'll do everything I can to help fix you," says Doc. "Then some lucky kid will take you home!"
12
"First I'm going to have to play the game to get you out of the tank."
"But Doc, this game is very difficult!" says the pink bear.

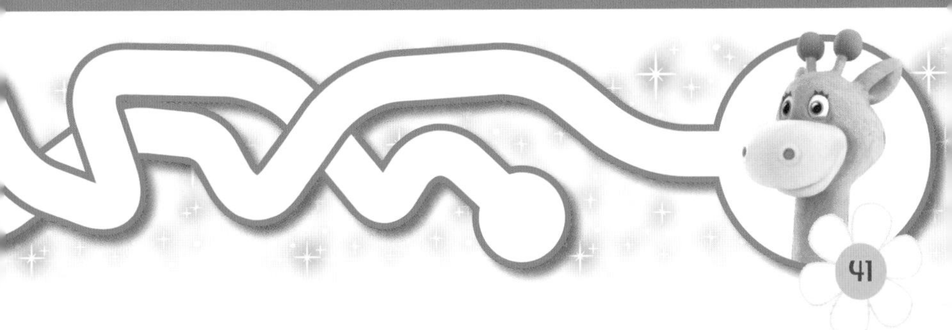

"It might be difficult, but we have to help Gaby," says Doc as she presses the start button. "Here we go!"

"To the left, right a bit ... there!" The grabber picks up Gaby and starts to lift but ... oh no! It drops her.

15

"This job needs a dragon!" says Stuffy bravely. "I'll climb in and hold onto Gaby as the grabber pulls me out."

"Really, Stuffy? That's so brave," says Doc. "Together we can do it!" "This dragon is going in!" yells Stuffy.

Let's sing together ...

Ouches can happen but don't you worry,
True friends will always help you in a hurry.

16

Stuffy holds Gaby and Doc lifts them out. They've done it! Now Doc must mend Gaby's leg.

17

Doc pushes the stuffing in and ties the thread. "You're all better!" "Thank you, Doc. Perhaps I will find a new home now," says Gaby.

18

"Come home with us," cries Doc. "That would be lovely," says Gaby, "but what about my friends in the tank?"

19

"Let's tell every kid in the arcade to come and win a toy," smiles Doc. "Soon all of your friends will have a happy new home!"

Well done, Doc, another Boo-Boo made better!

Search and Find

When Doc has a patient, she needs to look closely to work out what's wrong with them.

Look closely at the picture to find these things.

Can you find 10  in the picture?

Tick the boxes when you spot them.

How Many Tools?

Hallie is clearing up Doc's clinic. Help her count Doc's tools, then write the numbers in the boxes below.

Answers: Stethoscope - 1, Arm Cuff - 2, Thermometer - 3 and Hammer - 4.

Chilly Dot-to-Dot

Join the dots to complete Chilly, then colour in his hat, scarf and buttons!

Spot the Difference

These pictures look the same but 6 things are different in picture 2. Can you spot them all?

2

Answers:

Story

One Note

1

Donny and Alma are singing a song in the garden. Donny is playing his toy drums. Alma is playing her toy xylophone.

2

Doc thinks they sound great! She joins in the song on the kazoo. This band is really rocking!

3

"Wait, my xylophone sounds funny," says Alma. "One of the keys doesn't make the right sound, listen."
Thud! Thud! goes the key.
"That's not right, shall I take a look at it for you, Alma?" asks Doc.

Wonder

4

"Could you, Doc? Because our band won't work without my xylophone," says Alma sadly. "Don't worry, Alma, the Doc is in!" Doc carries the xylophone to her surgery and magics all her toys to life.

5

"Hello toys, we've got a musical patient who needs our help," says Doc. "Hi everyone, I'm Xyla the xylophone."

6

"I love dancing to music!" says Lambie as she hugs Xyla. "Don't worry, Doc will help you to feel better."

"I love music, too," shouts Stuffy. "Check this out - BOOM! Ch-Ka! BOOM! Ch-Ka! I'm a hip-hop dragon and I'm here to say, I love to ROOOARR every day!"

8

"You're a great rapper, Stuffy!" giggles Doc. "Now let's see if we can help Xyla to get her music back."

"Okay, Xyla, I'm going to use my stethoscope to hear how you sound. Hmm, I think I can see where the problem is," says Doc.
"Here's your magnifying glass, Doc," says Stuffy.
"Thanks, Stuffy ... aha! I have a diagnosis!" cries Doc.

How many musical notes are there in Xyla's song?

Count them up and write the answer in the box.

10

"What's the problem, Doc?" asks Hallie. "Xyla has Loose Key Syndrome. This screw is undone, so the key is loose."

"So it is," says Stuffy as he prods Xyla's key. Uh-oh, Stuffy has made the key fly through the air! It's heading for the sink!

11

"My key! It's fallen down the plug hole!" cries Xyla. "It's lost. Now I'll never play in Alma's band again."

12

"Sorry, Xyla," says Stuffy quietly. "It's okay, Stuffy, it was an accident," says Xyla, but she still looks upset.

13

"I know how you feel, Xyla," says Doc. "When I lost one of my baby teeth I was left with a hole and it looked funny. I sounded funny when I talked, too!"

14

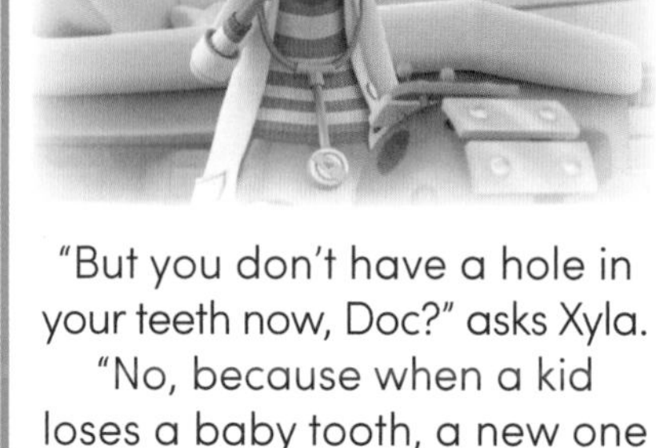

"But you don't have a hole in your teeth now, Doc?" asks Xyla. "No, because when a kid loses a baby tooth, a new one grows in its place."

15

"So I might grow a new key?" asks Xyla. "I think that only happens for kids, not for toys," says Doc. "Wait, I have an idea!"

"I have a special box of toy parts, let's see if there's something musical in there that might replace your lost key."

Let's make sounds like the instruments from the story ... TRUMPET XYLOPHONE CASTANET DRUMS

16

"Toot! Toot! A trumpet?" asks Stuffy.
"Click! Clack! A castanet?" asks Lambie.
"Hmm, they don't make the right sound."

17

"Look!" says Xyla. "There's a key hidden in the box! It's like the one I lost!"
"It looks good but will it fit?" asks Hallie.

18

"I need my special screwdriver," says Doc. It only takes a moment ... TING! Doc hits the key and it sounds perfect.

19

"Thanks, Doc, you rock!" cries Xyla. "Now let's rock to the music!" laughs Doc, and everyone starts to dance.

Odd Lambie Out

These 5 pictures of Lambie look the same, but one is different. Can you spot the odd one out?

Lambie picture c is the odd one out.

Chilly Count

How many pictures of Chilly can you see?
Add the number in the box.

There are ☐ Chilly pictures.

There are 8 Chilly pictures. Stuffy is also on the page.

Doc's Quiz

Do you want to be just like Doc?
See if you know the answers
to these questions.

1 Which toy gives the best cuddles?

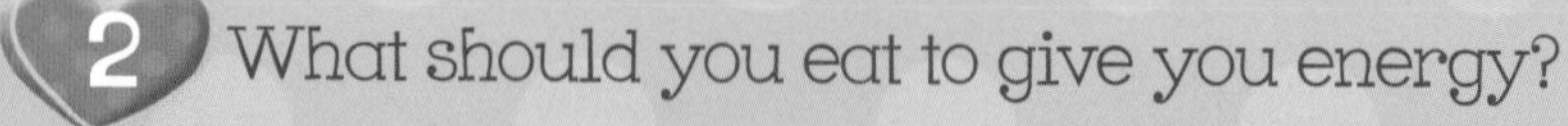

2 What should you eat to give you energy?

a. cardboard

b. fruit

c. nothing.

3 What should you do if you fall and cut yourself?

a. carry on playing

b. get an adult to clean and plaster it

c. go to the dentist.

4 If it's hot outside, what should you do?

a. drink lots of water

b. wear lots of clothes

c. bake a cake.

5 If it's cold outside, what should you do?

a. go swimming

b. wrap up warm

c. carry an umbrella.

6 If a friend feels sad, what should you do?

a. play with other friends

b. ask her what's wrong

c. tease her.

Answers: 1 = Lambie, 2 = b, 3 = b, 4 = a, 5 = b, 6 = b.

Goodbye!

Finish colouring the picture then wave goodbye to Doc and friends.